The Pandava Princes

THOUSANDS OF YEARS AGO, INDIA WAS DIVIDED INTO MANY SOVEREIGN STATES. ONE OF THEM WAS HASTINAPURA, RULED BY THE BLIND KING DHRITARASHTRA. HE HAD A HUNDRED SONS, WHO WERE CALLED THE KAURAVAS. THE ELDEST WAS DURYODHANA.

MW00954513

DHRITARASHTRA'S BROTHER PANDU, HAD RULED THE KINGDOM EARLIER, BUT HE HAD RETIRED TO THE FOREST, BECAUSE OF CONTINUED ILLNESS. PANDU HAD TWO WIVES—KUNTI AND MADRI. THERE IN COURSE OF TIME, THREE SONS WERE BORN TO KUNTI—YUDHISHTHIRA, BHEEMA AND ARJUNA. MADRI HAD TWO SONS—NAKULA AND SAHADEVA. TOGETHER THEY WERE CALLED THE PANDAVAS.

THE GREAT SAGES OF THE JUNGLE TAUGHT THE PANDAVAS TO READ AND WRITE.

BHEEMA!

YES., GURUDEV. I WILL BE THERE IN A MINUTE.

THE HARD JUNGLE LIFE MADE THEM STURDY AND FEARLESS.

2

WHEN PANDU DIED, MADRI BURNT HERSELF ON THE PYRE. SAGE VYASA CAME TO CONSOLE KUNTI.

DO NOT GRIEVE, KUNTI. I WILL ESCORT YOUR SONS TO HASTINAPURA.

ARJUNA ! I HEARD FROM MOTHER THAT WE ARE LEAVING FOR HASTINA-PURA TOMORROW

AT THE PALACE, YOU WILL MEET BHEESHMA, YOUR GREAT GRAND UNCLE, VIDURA, THE WISE MINISTER AND...

..OUR HUNDRED COUSINS! I WONDER HOW OUR UNCLE REMEMBERS THEIR NAMES!

NEXT DAY—

ARJUNA ! WILL WE GET SUCH A WARM WELCOME AT HASTINAPURA ALSO ?

VICTORY TO THE SONS OF PANDU !

ON THEIR WAY—

3

COME, MY SONS.

AT THE PALACE, THE BLIND KING DHRITARASHTRA WELCOMED THEM WITH A SHOW OF LOVE.

SONS INDEED! AND WHO ARE WE?

BHEESHMA, THEIR GREAT GRAND UNCLE, LOVED THEM AS MUCH AS HE DID THE KAURAVAS.

DUHSHASANA! DURYODHANA! LIVE TOGETHER AS BROTHERS WITH THE PANDAVAS.

BE WORTHY SONS OF THE GREAT PANDU.

VIDURA TOO, BLESSED THEM.

AS THE DAYS PASSED, DURYODHANA'S HATRED OF THE PANDAVAS GREW.

THIS YUDHISHTHIRA MAY ONE DAY BECOME THE CROWN PRINCE.

AN HONOUR WHICH IS YOURS BY RIGHT, DURYODHANA!

4

THE KAURAVAS ENVIED THE FIVE PRINCES.

SEE, HOW ARJUNA NEVER MISSES HIS MARK.

AND LOOK AT NAKULA! RIDING A HORSE!

DUHSHASANA! LOOK, HOW HE PULLS OUR BROTHERS!

THE KAURAVAS WERE ESPECIALLY AFRAID OF BHEEMA'S GREAT STRENGTH.

LIKE AN ELEPHANT DRAGGING TIMBER!

THE MORE FEATS HE PERFORMED, THE MORE HE WAS HATED.

BHEEMA HAS BEEN UNDER WATER FOR QUITE SOME TIME. I HOPE HE DOES NOT COME UP

DON'T SHAKE THE TREE, BHEEMA. WE MAY FALL DOWN!

LIKE DRIED LEAVES, EH!

DURING A PICNIC ON THE RIVER—

THE POISONED FOOD MADE BHEEMA DROWSY.

THEY TIED BHEEMA AND THREW HIM INTO THE RIVER

6

NEAR THE PALACE GATES, YUDHISHTHIRA MET DURYODHANA.

WHERE IS BHEEMA?

HE MUST BE IN THE PALACE. HE LEFT MUCH BEFORE US.

IN THE RIVER, BHEEMA ESCAPED THE IRON SPIKES, BUT THE SNAKES BIT HIM.

THE SNAKE POISON ACTED AGAINST THE POISONED FOOD WHICH HE HAD EATEN.

WHERE AM I?

HE TWITCHED HIS MUSCLES TILL THE BONDS BURST.

SOON HE CAME OUT OF THE WATER AND REACHED THE PALACE.

HELLO, DURYODHANA! THE SNAKES SEND YOU THEIR LOVE.

HOW DID HE SURVIVE?

THE BRAHMAN DID THE SAME THING WITH ANOTHER BLADE—THEN ANOTHER—AND ANOTHER, TILL A CHAIN WAS FORMED.

WHEN HE PULLED THE CHAIN, THE BALL CAME OUT WITH IT.

THE BRAHMAN SENT AN ARROW STRAIGHT INTO THE WELL. IT BOUNCED BACK BRINGING WITH IT THE PRECIOUS RING.

AT THE COURT, BHEESHMA RECOGNISED HIM. KING DHRITARASHTRA RECEIVED HIM WITH HONOUR.

DRONACHARYA! YOU ARE WELCOME, SIR!

I HAVE HEARD OF YOU. WHY DON'T YOU STAY WITH US AND BE A TUTOR TO THE PRINCES?

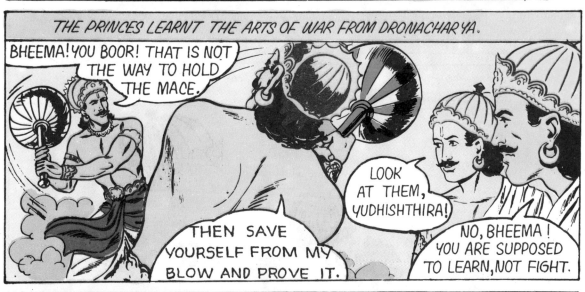

THE PRINCES LEARNT THE ARTS OF WAR FROM DRONACHARYA.

BHEEMA! YOU BOOR! THAT IS NOT THE WAY TO HOLD THE MACE.

THEN SAVE YOURSELF FROM MY BLOW AND PROVE IT.

LOOK AT THEM, YUDHISHTHIRA!

NO, BHEEMA! YOU ARE SUPPOSED TO LEARN, NOT FIGHT.

ONE DAY, DRONA HELD A CONTEST TO WHICH THE KING WAS INVITED. A BIG CROWD CAME TO WITNESS THE FEATS.

LOOK AT ARJUNA! HE NEVER MISSES HIS MARK!

I BET NO ONE CAN EQUAL HIM IN ARCHERY.

SUDDENLY, A YOUTH CLAD IN SHINING ARMOUR STEPPED FORWARD.

ARJUNA! I CHALLENGE YOU!

THIS MAN HAS PERFORMED ALL THE FEATS OF ARJUNA.

LOOK AT ARJUNA! HIS FACE HAS TURNED WHITE.

JUST THEN, A CHARIOTEER, WHO WAS AMONG THE SPECTATORS, ADVANCED WITH TEARS FLOWING DOWN HIS CHEEKS.

KARNA! MY SON! YOU HAVE BROUGHT GLORY TO ME.

A CHARIOTEER'S SON? POOH!

THAT BOW IS NOT FOR YOU. TAKE A WHIP!

DURYODHANA INSTANTLY TOOK A LIKING FOR KARNA. BY BEFRIENDING HIM, HE WANTED TO HUMILIATE ARJUNA.

FRIEND KARNA! I PROMISE YOU THE KINGDOM OF ANGA.

AFTER OBTAINING THE PERMISSION OF KING DHRITARASHTRA, KARNA WAS CROWNED THERE AND THEN.

HOW CAN I EVER REPAY YOUR KINDNESS, DURYODHANA!

THE QUICKNESS OF DURYODHANA'S ACTION ASTONISHED THE WHOLE GATHERING.

THAT DOES NOT SOLVE THE PROBLEM. HE CANNOT HIDE HIS LOW BIRTH.

COME, KARNA! DON'T LET ARJUNA'S REMARK BOTHER YOU.

KUNTI, WHO WITNESSED ALL THIS, WAS ALSO SAD.

HE IS MY SON! BUT WHEN HE WAS BORN I WAS SO YOUNG.

"I CAST HIM AWAY. THIS CHARIOTEER MUST HAVE FOUND HIM"

13

THE PANDAVA PRINCES WERE LOVED ALL OVER THE COUNTRY.

WE WANT YUDHISHTHIRA TO BE THE KING!

THE PANDAVAS ARE BRAVE AND HONEST.

DURYODHANA IS TOO CRUEL TO BE THE KING.

THIS TALK REACHED THE EARS OF DURYODHANA.

FATHER! THE PEOPLE WANT YUDHISHTHIRA TO BE CROWNED KING.

WILL WE HAVE TO LIVE ON THE CRUMBS THE PANDAVAS THROW AT US?

I SUGGEST, YOU SEND THEM AWAY ON SOME PRETEXT.

PREFERABLY, TO A PLACE FAR AWAY.

SO THE PANDAVAS WERE SENT TO VARANAVATI TO ATTEND THE FESTIVAL BEING HELD THERE.

DURYODHANA WHISPERED SOMETHING IN THE EARS OF PUROCHANA, A CLEVER BUT SLY ARCHITECT.

VIDURA WARNED YUDHISHTHIRA TO BE CAREFUL.

WELCOME TO THE PANDAVA PRINCES.

AT VARANAVATI—

WHEN PUROCHANA FINISHED BUILDING A GRAND PALACE FOR THE PANDAVAS, THEY MOVED INTO IT.

WHAT A WORK OF ART!

ART INDEED! IT'S BUILT WITH ...LAC.

THIS CONTAINS JUTE...

THE PANDAVAS WERE CORRECT.

EVEN THIS ARTIFICIAL GARDEN HAS FLOWERS AND LEAVES OF WAX.

WE ARE CAUGHT IN A TRAP.

EVERY DAY THEY WENT HUNTING AND MADE THEMSELVES FAMILIAR WITH THE PATHS OF THE JUNGLE.

WHEN PUROCHANA SETS FIRE TO THE PALACE WE SHALL TAKE SHELTER HERE.

BUT WHY WAIT FOR HIM TO SET IT ON FIRE?

ONE DAY—

I AM A MINER! ACHARYA VIDURA HAS SENT ME TO HELP YOU.

THANK YOU.

THE MINER HAS DONE A GOOD JOB OF THIS TUNNEL.

IN A MATTER OF MINUTES, THE WHOLE PALACE WAS REDUCED TO ASHES. PUROCHANA WAS BURNT ALIVE IN THE TRAP WHICH HE HIMSELF HAD SET.

17

WHEN THE NEWS REACHED HASTINAPURA, DURYODHANA AND DUHSHASANA WERE HAPPY. SHAKUNI, THEIR WICKED UNCLE, CAUTIONED THEM.

BE CALM! YOU MUST NOT SHOW YOUR JOY.

YES. WE MUST MOURN FOR OUR DEAR DEPARTED COUSINS.

MEANWHILE, THE PANDAVAS, VERY MUCH ALIVE, TRUDGED THROUGH THE JUNGLE. WHEN KUNTI COULD WALK NO LONGER, BHEEMA CARRIED HER ON HIS SHOULDERS.

HE EVEN TOOK NAKULA AND SAHADEVA ON HIS HIPS.

LATE IN THE EVENING, THE NEXT DAY, THEY REACHED THE RIVER GANGA. GREETINGS FROM ACHARYA VIDURA. HE ASKED ME TO WAIT FOR YOU.

AFTER CROSSING THE RIVER, THEY ENTERED A DENSE FOREST.

I CAN'T WALK ANY FURTHER!

THEY LAY DOWN TO REST. BHEEMA ALONE STAYED AWAKE.

THIS WATER WILL REFRESH THEM. I WILL REMAIN AWAKE AND GUARD THEM.

FOR MANY DAYS THEY WANDERED. UP AND DOWN THE HILLS, THEY TREKKED. AT LAST IT SEEMED THAT THEY WERE NEAR SOME HUMAN HABITATION.

THERE! LET US GO AND ASK THEM FOR FOOD AND SHELTER!

NO, NAKULA! DON'T YOU SEE — THEY ARE RAKSHASAS!!

BUT THE RAKSHASAS WERE SOON ON THEIR TRAIL. BHEEMA FACED THEM WITH AN UPROOTED TREE.

HIDAMBASURA, THE RAKSHASA CHIEF, STEPPED FORWARD AND TRIED TO SNATCH THE TREE FROM BHEEMA'S HAND.

A FIERCE DUEL FOLLOWED...

... IN WHICH HIDIMBASURA WAS KILLED.

SOON—

THEY WANT YOU TO GO WITH THEM AND BE THEIR KING.

THE PANDAVAS ACCOMPANIED THEM TO THEIR VILLAGE AND THERE BHEEMA MARRIED HIDIMBAA THE SISTER OF HIDIMBA.

THESE RAKSHASAS ARE NOT SUCH A BAD LOT AFTER ALL, YUDHISHTHIRA!

AFTER SOME DAYS—

BHEEMA! I DON'T LIKE THIS PLACE. LET US GO SOMEWHERE ELSE.

AS YOU WISH, BROTHER!

WHAT IS THE NAME OF THIS TOWN, GOOD MAN?

EKACHAKRAPURA AND YOU ARE WELCOME, GOOD BRAHMANS!

GOOD! HE THINKS WE ARE BRAHMANS.

AFTER A LONG JOURNEY—

21

IN EKACHAKRAPURA, THE PANDAVAS LIVED IN THE HOUSE OF A POOR BRAHMAN. ONE DAY—

WHAT IS THE MATTER, GOOD BRAHMAN?

THIS LITTLE DAUGHTER OF OURS WILL SOON BE EATEN BY BAKASURA, WHO LIVES IN A CAVE OUTSIDE THE VILLAGE.

"HE HAS EXTRACTED TERMS UNDER WHICH PEOPLE HAVE TO SEND HIM A CART-LOAD OF FOOD EVERY DAY. HE EATS THE DRIVER AND BULLOCKS ALSO, ALONG WITH THE FOOD."

I WOULD RATHER GO MYSELF THAN SACRIFICE THIS INNOCENT GIRL.

OH, NO! IF YOU GO, WHO WILL LOOK AFTER THE FAMILY? I WILL GO.

LET ME GO, MOTHER. I WILL KILL THE RAKSHASA WITH A STICK.

YOU MUST DO SOMETHING ABOUT IT, SON!

LATER—

AS YOU WISH, MOTHER!

22

BHEEMA DROVE THE CART OF FOOD TO THE BORDER OF THE TOWN. PEOPLE FLOCKED TO SEE HIM OFF.

HE LOOKS POWERFUL!

BUT BAKASURA MAY KILL HIM

WHEN BHEEMA REACHED THE MOUTH OF THE CAVE, HE UNYOKED THE OXEN AND SAT DOWN TO A HEARTY MEAL

ONCE THE FIGHT STARTS, ALL THE FOOD WILL BE SCATTERED. I MUST FINISH IT QUICKLY.

WHEN BAKASURA CAME OUT OF THE CAVE, HE WAS ENRAGED AT WHAT HE SAW.

IT SEEMS AS IF SOME NUTS ARE FALLING ON MY BACK.

23

OH! IT IS THE RAKSHASA! HE IS BECOMING A NUISANCE.

THIS POT OF BUTTER MILK TASTES GOOD.

AFTER THE MEAL BHEEMA LIFTED THE GIANT AND HURLED HIM VIOLENTLY ON THE GROUND.

BAKASURA DIED ON THE SPOT.

BHEEMA DRAGGED THE DEAD BODY OF THE GIANT TO THE GATE OF THE CITY AND QUIETLY WENT HOME.

A FEW DAYS LATER THE PANDAVAS HEARD EXCITING NEWS—

I HEAR KING DRUPADA IS ARRANGING A TEST OF ARCHERY.

...YES.., AND THERE WILL BE GIFTS FOR US.

THE BEST ARCHER WILL WIN THE HAND OF DRAUPADI.

MOTHER! MAY WE GO AND ATTEND THE MARRIAGE?

YES, ARJUNA.

THE PANDAVAS SOON REACHED THE CAPITAL WHICH WAS GAILY DECORATED.

IN THE PALACE HALL, HUNDREDS OF PRINCES WERE SEATED. THE PANDAVAS TOOK THEIR SEATS IN THE ENCLOSURE MEANT FOR BRAHMANS.

THIS, MY SISTER, IS KING SHISHUPALA OF CHEDI.

THIS IS DHRISHTADYUMNA, THE BROTHER OF DRAUPADI, INTRODUCING THE GUESTS.

25

THE INTRODUCTIONS OVER, DHRISHTADYUMNA ANNOUNCED—

FRIENDS! HERE ARE A BOW AND ARROWS AND THERE, ABOVE THE REVOLVING WHEEL IS THE TARGET—A FISH. YOU HAVE TO HIT THE EYE OF THE FISH, LOOKING AT ITS REFLECTION IN THE WATER BELOW. WHO EVER DOES THIS FIVE TIMES IN SUCCESSION, SHALL WIN THE BRIDE.

THE PRINCES TRIED ONE AFTER ANOTHER BUT NONE COULD LIFT THE HEAVY BOW.

THIS IS NO BOW! NO MAN CAN WIN THE TEST!!

DURYODHANA FELL TO THE GROUND WHEN HE TRIED TO LIFT THE BOW. LORD KRISHNA LOOKED MEANINGFULLY AT ARJUNA, HIS COUSIN.

ARJUNA GOT UP FROM THE ENCLOSURE OF BRAHMANS.

WITH THE PERMISSION OF DHRISHTADYUMNA, HE LIFTED THE BOW, STRUNG IT, AND SENT FIVE ARROWS IN QUICK SUCCESSION.

EVERY ARROW OF HIS HAS HIT THE TARGET.

FANTASTIC!!

DRAUPADI GARLANDED HIM.

THERE WAS AN UPROAR IN THE HALL.

DURYODHANA! WE SHOULD NOT TOLERATE THIS!

YES, SHISHUPALA. IT IS A DISGRACE TO US ALL.

MANY OF THE PRINCES RUSHED TO THE DAIS. BHEEMA CAME TO HELP ARJUNA.

IF ANYONE COMES ONE STEP FURTHER, I WILL SMASH HIS SKULL.

IN THE CONFUSION THAT FOLLOWED, ARJUNA AND HIS BROTHERS WITH THE NEWLY-WON-BRIDE, LEFT FOR EKACHAKRAPURA. KING DRUPADA, HOWEVER, WAS WORRIED.

WHO COULD THIS BRAVE BRAHMAN BE?

FATHER! I'LL FOLLOW THEM AND FIND OUT

ARJUNA WAS EAGER TO BREAK THE NEWS TO HIS MOTHER.

MOTHER! SEE WHAT WE HAVE BROUGHT TODAY.

WHATEVER IT IS ARJUNA, YOU SHOULD SHARE IT EQUALLY AMONG YOU.

THEY ARE THE PANDAVAS!

DHRISHTADYUMNA TOLD HIS FATHER ALL THAT HE SAW IN EKACHAKRAPURA.

FIVE HUSBANDS! I DON'T LIKE THE IDEA. HOWEVER, BRING THEM HERE WITH HONOUR.

WHEN THE NEWS REACHED HASTINAPURA—

YUDHISHTHIRA AND BHEEMA, ALIVE!

AND GROWN STRONGER TOO. DRUPADA HAS A LARGE ARMY.

LET US ATTACK DRUPADA AND FINISH HIM AND HIS FIVE SONS-IN-LAW!

BHEESHMA AND VIDURA ADVISED DHRITARASHTRA—

BRING THEM WITH HONOUR TO HASTINAPURA.

NO, FATHER! I WILL NEVER TOLERATE THIS!

GIVE THEM HALF THE KINGDOM AND LET THEM RULE FROM KHANDAVAPRASTHA.

I HATE THEM! I HATE THEM! I WANT TO RUN AWAY FROM HERE.

PLEASE PUT ON A SMILE! WE MUST PRETEND TO WELCOME THEM.

THE PANDAVAS WERE INVITED TO HASTINAPURA

A FEW DAYS AFTER THEIR TRIUMPHANT RETURN, THE PANDAVAS LEFT FOR KHANDAVAPRASTHA TO BUILD A NEW CITY.

THEY RULED FROM INDRAPRASTHA FOR MANY YEARS. LORD KRISHNA WAS THEIR FRIEND AND ADVISER. ONE DAY—

ONLY IF YOU DEFEAT THE WICKED KING JARASANDHA WILL OTHER PRINCES ACKNOWLEDGE YOU AS THEIR LEADER.

BUT KRISHNA! HOW CAN WE DEFEAT JARASANDHA?

LET'S GO TO MAGADHA AND CHALLENGE HIM TO A DUEL.

I ACCEPT THE CHALLENGE! I SHALL FIGHT.

DISGUISED AS BRAHMANS, KRISHNA, BHEEMA AND ARJUNA REACHED THE PALACE OF JARASANDHA.

IN THE FIERCE FIGHT THAT FOLLOWED, JARASANDHA WAS KILLED BY BHEEMA.

BHEEMA RETURNED IN TRIUMPH TO INDRAPRASTHA. KINGS FROM ALL OVER THE COUNTRY GATHERED TO ATTEND THE RAJASUYA SACRIFICE BUT—

LORD KRISHNA! THE FIRST HONOUR ON THIS OCCASION SHOULD GO TO YOU.

I OBJECT TO KRISHNA GETTING THE PLACE OF HONOUR.

DO SO SHISHUPALA! BUT NOT WITH YOUR SWORD.

AS SHISHUPALA MADE AN ASSAULT ON KRISHNA, THE DISCUS OF KRISHNA CUT OFF HIS HEAD.

AND THE RAJASUYA WAS COMPLETED WHICH MADE THE PANDAVAS SUPREME IN THE COUNTRY.

VICTORY TO KRISHNA!

VICTORY TO YUDHISHTHIRA!